Stunt Show!

By Ace Landers

Illustrated by Dave White

SCHOLASTIC INC.

New York   Toronto   London   Auckland   Sydney
Mexico City   New Delhi   Hong Kong   Buenos Aires

ISBN-13: 978-0-545-08506-9
ISBN-10: 0-545-08506-3

12 11 10   40   11 12/0

Book design: Henry Ng and Cheung Tai
Printed in the U.S.A.   109
First printing, November 2008

It is a stunt show!

Look at all the tracks!
The cars will do stunts.

These drivers went to stunt school.

The red car zooms around the track.

It is a high-speed chase!

6

There is a ramp ahead.

The blue car races toward the ramp.

The ramp is big.

The blue car flies
through the air.

Everyone cheers!

What a stunt!

The cars charge ahead.

Get ready to blast off!

There are two loops in
the middle of the track.

The cars drive fast.

They are in the loops.

This car will jump on a ramp.

The other cars will jump, too.

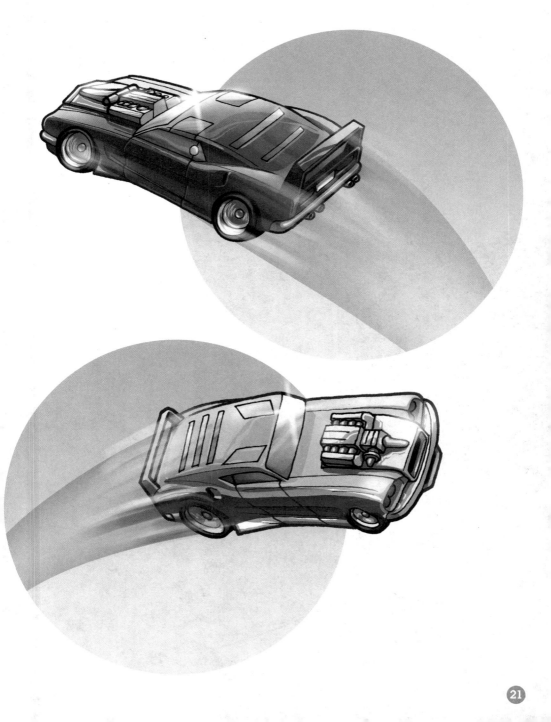

All four cars pass each other in the air!

Will they land safely?

They all land safely!

There is one last stunt.

The car drives at top speed.

The car flies through
a giant ring of fire!

Stunt driving is cool!